Mystery Solvers

TIME THIEF

Bath · New York · Singapore · Hong Kong · Cologne · Delhi · Melbourne

Written by Moira Butterfield
Detective Dog and comic illustrations by Jan Smith
Scene illustrations by Andy Everitt-Stewart

First published by Parragon in 2007

Parragon
Queen Street House
4 Queen Street
Bath BA1 1HE, UK

ISBN 978-1-4054-9544-8

Printed in China
Please retain this information for future reference.

MYSTERY SOLVER
MAGNIFY THE MYSTERY!

Hi there! My name is Detective Dog.

I collect mysteries, passed on to me by other dogs.

Dogs see, smell, and dig better than anyone. They make great detectives.

Mysteries have been going on for centuries. I know because a **TIME TRAVELER** told me!

My mysteries can only be solved by looking at tiny details.

Good luck. **Woof!**

You can do it, too, by using your brains and your magnifying glass.

THE ANSWERS ARE AT THE BACK, BUT GOOD DETECTIVES DON'T LOOK UNTIL THE END.

MUSEUM MADNESS!

This story was told to me by my dog friend, Kimmy. She belongs to Katie.

KATIE

SAM

KIMMY

ONE MORNING, WHEN KATIE AND KIMMY WERE VISITING SAM AT WORK, THEY NOTICED THAT A GOLD STATUE WAS MISSING. SAM TOLD THE MUSEUM DIRECTOR THE BAD NEWS.

Legend has it that the statue opens up doors to the past.

Never mind the legend—the statue is worth a fortune!

We'll help you find it. Kimmy is great at looking for clues and I have a magnifying glass. Let's go, Kimmy!

You can help Katie and Kimmy by finding these important clues in the museum.

A yellow hankie dropped by the thief.

Six handprints.

A watch dropped by the thief.

A piece of torn paper containing part of a message.

I A modern red purse

Help Katie's dad, Sam, check that nothing else has been stolen. Can you find these valuable objects still in the museum?

- A small painting of a king's dog
- A Roman emperor's ruby ring
- A gold slipper
- A gladiator's sword
- A famous U.S. president's pair of glasses

Use your magnifying glass here to find out what else Kimmy is searching for.

A security guard has secretly brought a pet into the museum. Kimmy has seen it. Can you see where it is!

CRAZY CASTLE!

Katie, Kimmy, and Sam looked around the museum for clues. The thief's trail led to an old mirror on the wall.

KIMMY PUT HER NOSE AGAINST THE MIRROR AND, SUDDENLY, THEY ALL FELL THROUGH IT.

This is fascinating! We're inside the walls of a medieval castle.

We've traveled through time! The legend of the statue was true.

Where has the thief gone? We need to find some clues, Kimmy.

Someone has stolen the cook's pie. Kimmy has sniffed them out. Can you find someone eating a pie in the scene?

Sam has made a checklist of some of the things he saw at the castle. Can you find them?

- A broken sword
- A kitten
- A lady sewing
- A dragon
- A fish

You can help Katie and Kimmy by finding these important clues in the castle.

Three blobs of chewing gum dropped by the thief.

Eight footprints from a sneaker.

2 A crown from a castle

A piece of torn paper containing part of a message.

ROMAN RUNAROUND!

The footprints in the castle led Kimmy and friends to a small door in the castle wall.

WHEN KATIE OPENED THE DOOR, THE MYSTERY SOLVERS FELL THROUGH TIME ONCE AGAIN.

We've followed the thief to an ancient Roman feast!

This is amazing!

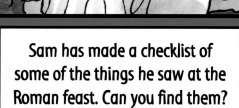

Woof!

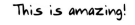

Sam has made a checklist of some of the things he saw at the Roman feast. Can you find them?

- An emperor's portrait on a brooch
- A lost Roman earring
- Someone wearing a helmet over his face
- A golden scroll
- An eagle

You can help Katie and Kimmy by finding these important clues.

A newspaper left by the thief.

3. A jar of Roman coins

A piece of torn paper containing part of a message.

A glimpse of a bare foot as the thief disappears.

A sneaker lost by the thief.

A greedy Roman has stolen a golden goblet from the feast and put it in his robe. Who is it? Kimmy has seen him.

WILD WEST!

Kimmy led Katie and Sam to a Roman fountain, and jumped through! Katie and Sam were quick to follow.

SOON, THE THREE SUPER SLEUTHS FOUND THEMSELVES IN A DIFFERENT CENTURY.

I think we're in a Wild West town, about a hundred and twenty years ago. It looks like an old movie!

The thief must be here somewhere. Let's find some more clues.

LOON

You can help Katie and Kimmy by finding these important clues.

A candy dropped by the thief.

A baseball cap left behind by the thief.

A piece of torn paper containing part of a message.

4 A cowboy's hat

Sam made a checklist of some of the things he saw in the Wild West town. Can you find them?

- A cowboy fast asleep
- A horseshoe
- A snake
- Someone mending a cowboy boot
- A man in a tin bathtub

STORES

A player is hiding the ace of hearts card during a card game. Can you see where? Kimmy has seen it.

LAND OF THE DINOSAURS!

Kimmy caught the scent of the thief. She quickly led Katie and Sam to a blacksmith.

THROUGH A BACK DOOR, THEY WALKED INTO THE WORLD OF DINOSAURS.

This is the time when T.rex lived. We'd better watch out!

Quickly, Kimmy! Follow the clues to find the thief!

You can help Katie and Kimmy by finding these important clues.

A comb dropped by the thief.

Six muddy handprints.

5. A dinosaur egg

A piece of torn paper containing part of a message.

Sam made a checklist of some of the things he saw in the world of the dinosaurs. Can you find them?

- A dinosaur baby hatching
- A dinosaur bone
- A blue dragonfly
- A dinosaur stepping on a flower
- A blue-and-purple dinosaur

Kimmy finds a nest of dinosaur eggs with one missing. Can you see the egg stealer?

13

VIKING VILLAGE!

Kimmy tracked down the thief and led them into a swamp!

Yuck! That has to be the grossest way to travel through time!

I'd rather dive into a swamp than get chomped by a T.rex!

THE MYSTERY SOLVERS LANDED IN SCANDINAVIA.

We're in a Viking village from over a thousand years ago!

14

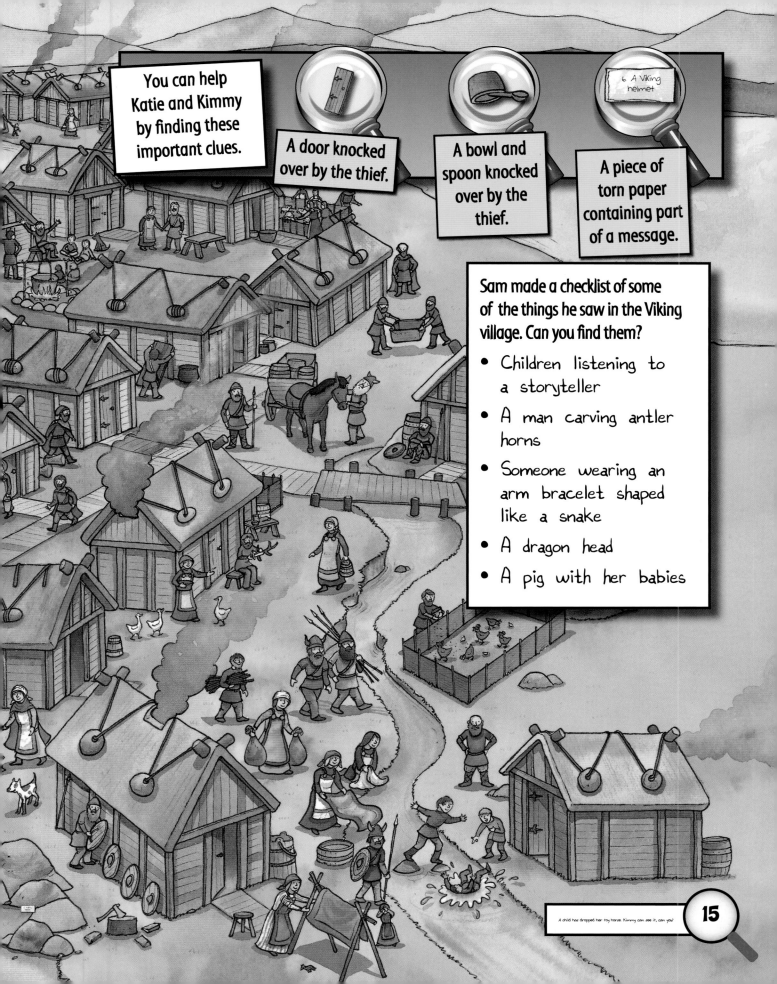

You can help Katie and Kimmy by finding these important clues.

A door knocked over by the thief.

A bowl and spoon knocked over by the thief.

6 A Viking helmet

A piece of torn paper containing part of a message.

Sam made a checklist of some of the things he saw in the Viking village. Can you find them?

- Children listening to a storyteller
- A man carving antler horns
- Someone wearing an arm bracelet shaped like a snake
- A dragon head
- A pig with her babies

A child has dropped her toy horse. Kimmy can see it, can you?

SO SHAKESPEARE!

Kimmy led the others toward a Viking boat.

KIMMY, KATIE, AND SAM STEPPED ONTO THE BOAT, AND SLIPPED THROUGH TIME AGAIN.

This is Shakespeare's theater, the Globe! Look, his actors are rehearsing a play.

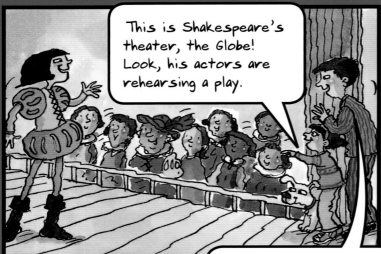

That means we're in England but about four hundred years ago.

I'd like to stay and watch, but we need to follow that thief!

You can help Katie and Kimmy by finding these important clues.

A hat knocked over by the thief.

The thief's hand as he slips away into another time.

7. Shakespeare's quill pen

A piece of torn paper containing part of a message.

Sam made a checklist of some of the things he saw in Shakespeare's theater. Can you find them?

- Someone asleep
- A scroll
- Someone counting the money made from yesterday's play
- Someone mending a costume

Kimmy notices that an actor from another theater is spying on the play! Can you see the spy!

STONE AGE SURPRISE!

The team slipped through a back door and found themselves in the Stone Age, 40,000 years ago!

STONE AGE PEOPLE HUNTED WOOLLY MAMMOTHS. THEY USED THEIR BONES AND SKINS TO BUILD HOUSES. IN MODERN TIMES, THIS PART OF THE WORLD IS RUSSIA.

Brrr! It's very cold! I don't want to stay here long!

Come on, Kimmy. We can't be too far behind the thief now.

One of the Stone Age people has lost a boot. Can you find someone wearing just one boot?

Sam made a checklist of some of the things he saw in the Stone Age. Can you find them?

- A woolly mammoth still alive
- A necklace made of teeth
- An ax made of stone and antlers
- A bowl of nuts collected from the wood
- A sleeping dog
- A deer

You can help Katie and Kimmy by finding these important clues.

A pair of glasses left by the thief.

An empty bottle of water left by the thief.

8 A Stone Age boot

A piece of torn paper containing part of a message.

RAILROAD ROBBERY!

Kimmy saw the thief just as he vanished into a cave. The team were quick to follow.

THIS TIME KIMMY, KATIE, AND SAM STEPPED OUT ONTO A BUSY RAILROAD STATION—IN THE 1800s!

Look at those beautiful old steam trains.

Never mind the steam trains! Where's the thief?

You can help Katie and Kimmy by finding these important clues.

Some keys left by the thief.

A suitcase knocked over by the thief.

9. A Victorian umbrella

A piece of torn paper containing part of a message.

Sam made a checklist of some of the
things he saw in the train station.
Can you find them?

- Someone tying a shoe
- A red flag
- A cat fast asleep
- A man with a bird on his hat
- A flower-shape button.

Who is wearing odd shoes? Kimmy has found them. Can you?

INTO THE FUTURE!

The mystery solvers hopped onto a train and, this time, the path took an unexpected twist— into the **FUTURE!**

I think we're on a space station.

That means we've traveled into the future.

You can help Katie and Kimmy by finding these important clues.

A security alarm set off by the thief.

The thief's other shoe. (He lost the first one in the ancient Roman era.)

10. A space helmet

A piece of torn paper containing part of a message.

Sam made a checklist of some of the things he saw in the space station of the future. Can you find them?

- A picture of Earth
- An astronaut doing his homework
- An astronaut vacuuming
- An astronaut fast asleep
- An astrodog

Three spiders accidentally traveled into space with the astronauts. Kimmy has found them. Can you?

23

ANCIENT EGYPT!

The team hopped into a space shuttle and traveled through time again.

THE MYSTERY SOLVERS WERE ABOUT TO CATCH THE THIEF AT LAST IN ANCIENT EGYPT.

There's the Pharaoh, ruler of Ancient Egypt!

KATIE PUT TOGETHER THE PIECES OF THE MESSAGE SHE FOUND ALONG THE WAY. IT WAS A LIST OF THINGS TO STEAL! THE THIEF HAD DROPPED THE ITEMS IN ANCIENT EGYPT AS HE TRIED TO GET AWAY.

Can you help Katie and Kimmy find the stolen goods on this list in the picture?

I want the following things stolen for me.

1. A modern red purse
2. A crown from a castle
3. A jar of Roman coins
4. A cowboy's hat
5. A dinosaur egg
6. A Viking helmet
7. Shakespeare's quill pen
8. A Stone Age boot
9. A Victorian umbrella
10. A space helmet

I'll lend you a statue that will help you travel through time. I'll pay you well.

The boss

So the thief is working on someone else's orders. Who could it be?

MEANWHILE, THE PHARAOH WAS ANGRY. A VALUABLE NECKLACE IN THE SHAPE OF A SCARAB BEETLE HAD BEEN STOLEN. IT WAS ONE OF A PAIR. HE STILL HAD THE OTHER ONE.

The scarab beetle necklace!

Hmm. I've seen someone wearing a scarab necklace just like that.

CASE CLOSED!

At last the team arrived back in the museum.

THIS TIME KIMMY CAUGHT THE THIEF.

AND KATIE CONFRONTED THE MUSEUM DIRECTOR...

You're wearing a scarab necklace you stole from a pharaoh. It matches the one I've just seen in Ancient Egypt.

KATIE WORKED OUT THAT THE MUSEUM DIRECTOR HAD HIRED A THIEF AND LENT HIM THE GOLD STATUE TO STEAL THINGS THROUGH TIME. LUCKILY, THE MYSTERY SOLVERS NOTICED THE STATUE WAS MISSING IN THE MUSEUM, AND WERE ABLE TO WORK THROUGH THE CLUES TO SOLVE THE CRIME.

THE MUSEUM DIRECTOR ESCAPED! SHE RAN THROUGH THE MUSEUM, OPENING DOORS THAT HAVE THE NUMBERS 3, 4, AND 5 IN THEIR SECURITY CODE.

Can you help the team find six doors that the museum director opened? Then can you find her hiding place? Use your magnifying glass to read the numbers. Start at the top of the stairs on the first floor.

START HERE

THE MUSEUM DIRECTOR AND HER HIRED THIEF WERE CAUGHT. THE GOLD STATUE WAS RETURNED TO THE MUSEUM AND GUARDED BY SECURITY.

Well done, everyone. I hope we didn't change history on our time travels!

But someone back in time DID find a modern-day object dropped by the thief. Can you go back through the book and find out who it was?

ANSWERS

Pages 4–5
- ○ Sam's checklist
- ○ Important clues
- ○ Kimmy's mini finds

Pages 6–7
- ○ Sam's checklist
- ○ Important clues
- ○ Kimmy's mini finds

Pages 8–9
- ○ Sam's checklist
- ○ Important clues
- ○ Kimmy's mini finds

ANSWERS

Pages 16–17
- ◯ Sam's checklist
- ◯ Important clues
- ◯ Kimmy's mini finds

Pages 18–19
- ◯ Sam's checklist
- ◯ Important clues
- ◯ Kimmy's mini finds

Pages 20–21
- ◯ Sam's checklist
- ◯ Important clues
- ◯ Kimmy's mini finds

Turn to page 32 to find the answers to the museum maze.

ANSWERS

Pages 26–27

—— Route taken

○ Museum director

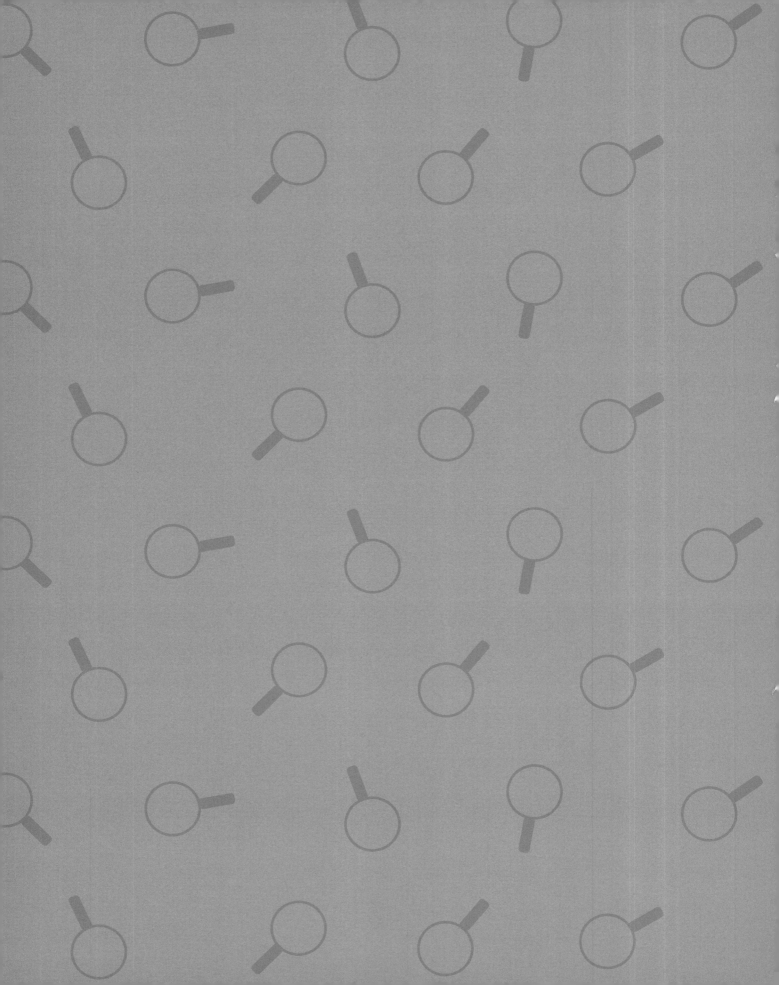